Higher Scores on Science Standardized Tests, G

MW00861509

STUDENT'S NAME

LAST	FIRST	MI
B a l a s a	M a t t	M

MONTH Jan, Feb, Mar, Apr, May, Jun, Jul, Aug, Sep, Oct, Nov, Dec

DAY — **YEAR**

GRADE ② ③ ● ⑤ ⑥

**Higher Scores on Science
Standardized Tests, Grade 3
© Steck-Vaughn Company**

Overall Assessment

1. Ⓐ Ⓑ Ⓒ   3. Ⓐ Ⓑ Ⓒ   5. Ⓐ Ⓑ Ⓒ   7. Ⓐ Ⓑ Ⓒ   9. Ⓐ Ⓑ Ⓒ   11. Ⓐ Ⓑ Ⓒ   13. Ⓐ Ⓑ Ⓒ
2. Ⓐ Ⓑ Ⓒ   4. Ⓐ Ⓑ Ⓒ   6. Ⓐ Ⓑ Ⓒ   8. Ⓐ Ⓑ Ⓒ   10. Ⓐ Ⓑ Ⓒ   12. Ⓐ Ⓑ Ⓒ   14. Ⓐ Ⓑ Ⓒ

Life Science Pretest

1. Ⓐ Ⓑ Ⓒ   2. Ⓐ Ⓑ Ⓒ   3. Ⓐ Ⓑ Ⓒ   4. Ⓐ Ⓑ Ⓒ   5. Ⓐ Ⓑ Ⓒ   6. Ⓐ Ⓑ Ⓒ   7. Ⓐ Ⓑ Ⓒ

Earth Science Pretest

1. Ⓐ Ⓑ Ⓒ   2. Ⓐ Ⓑ Ⓒ   3. Ⓐ Ⓑ Ⓒ   4. Ⓐ Ⓑ Ⓒ   5. Ⓐ Ⓑ Ⓒ   6. Ⓐ Ⓑ Ⓒ   7. Ⓐ Ⓑ Ⓒ

Physical Science Pretest

1. Ⓐ Ⓑ Ⓒ   2. Ⓐ Ⓑ Ⓒ   3. Ⓐ Ⓑ Ⓒ   4. Ⓐ Ⓑ Ⓒ   5. Ⓐ Ⓑ Ⓒ   6. Ⓐ Ⓑ Ⓒ   7. Ⓐ Ⓑ Ⓒ

Life Science Posttest

1. Ⓐ Ⓑ Ⓒ   3. Ⓐ Ⓑ Ⓒ   5. Ⓐ Ⓑ Ⓒ   7. Ⓐ Ⓑ Ⓒ   9. Ⓐ Ⓑ Ⓒ   11. Ⓐ Ⓑ Ⓒ   13. Ⓐ Ⓑ Ⓒ
2. Ⓐ Ⓑ Ⓒ   4. Ⓐ Ⓑ Ⓒ   6. Ⓐ Ⓑ Ⓒ   8. Ⓐ Ⓑ Ⓒ   10. Ⓐ Ⓑ Ⓒ   12. Ⓐ Ⓑ Ⓒ   14. Ⓐ Ⓑ Ⓒ

Earth Science Posttest

1. Ⓐ Ⓑ Ⓒ   3. Ⓐ Ⓑ Ⓒ   5. Ⓐ Ⓑ Ⓒ   7. Ⓐ Ⓑ Ⓒ   9. Ⓐ Ⓑ Ⓒ   11. Ⓐ Ⓑ Ⓒ   13. Ⓐ Ⓑ Ⓒ
2. Ⓐ Ⓑ Ⓒ   4. Ⓐ Ⓑ Ⓒ   6. Ⓐ Ⓑ Ⓒ   8. Ⓐ Ⓑ Ⓒ   10. Ⓐ Ⓑ Ⓒ   12. Ⓐ Ⓑ Ⓒ   14. Ⓐ Ⓑ Ⓒ

Physical Science Posttest

1. Ⓐ Ⓑ Ⓒ   3. Ⓐ Ⓑ Ⓒ   5. Ⓐ Ⓑ Ⓒ   7. Ⓐ Ⓑ Ⓒ   9. Ⓐ Ⓑ Ⓒ   11. Ⓐ Ⓑ Ⓒ   13. Ⓐ Ⓑ Ⓒ
2. Ⓐ Ⓑ Ⓒ   4. Ⓐ Ⓑ Ⓒ   6. Ⓐ Ⓑ Ⓒ   8. Ⓐ Ⓑ Ⓒ   10. Ⓐ Ⓑ Ⓒ   12. Ⓐ Ⓑ Ⓒ   14. Ⓐ Ⓑ Ⓒ

Life, part 1   1. Ⓐ Ⓑ Ⓒ   2. Ⓐ Ⓑ Ⓒ   3. Ⓐ Ⓑ Ⓒ   4. Ⓐ Ⓑ Ⓒ   5. Ⓐ Ⓑ Ⓒ   6. Ⓐ Ⓑ Ⓒ

Life, part 2   1. Ⓐ Ⓑ Ⓒ   2. Ⓐ Ⓑ Ⓒ   3. Ⓐ Ⓑ Ⓒ   4. Ⓐ Ⓑ Ⓒ   5. Ⓐ Ⓑ Ⓒ   6. Ⓐ Ⓑ Ⓒ

Earth, part 1   1. Ⓐ Ⓑ Ⓒ   2. Ⓐ Ⓑ Ⓒ   3. Ⓐ Ⓑ Ⓒ   4. Ⓐ Ⓑ Ⓒ   5. Ⓐ Ⓑ Ⓒ   6. Ⓐ Ⓑ Ⓒ

Earth, part 2   1. Ⓐ Ⓑ Ⓒ   2. Ⓐ Ⓑ Ⓒ   3. Ⓐ Ⓑ Ⓒ   4. Ⓐ Ⓑ Ⓒ   5. Ⓐ Ⓑ Ⓒ   6. Ⓐ Ⓑ Ⓒ

Physical, part 1   1. Ⓐ Ⓑ Ⓒ   2. Ⓐ Ⓑ Ⓒ   3. Ⓐ Ⓑ Ⓒ   4. Ⓐ Ⓑ Ⓒ   5. Ⓐ Ⓑ Ⓒ

Physical, part 2   1. Ⓐ Ⓑ Ⓒ   2. Ⓐ Ⓑ Ⓒ   3. Ⓐ Ⓑ Ⓒ   4. Ⓐ Ⓑ Ⓒ   5. Ⓐ Ⓑ Ⓒ   6. Ⓐ Ⓑ Ⓒ

Overall Assessment

Your Score: _____

Directions Darken the circle by the answer that correctly completes each statement.

⏱ **You have 25 minutes.**

1. People have five senses: sight, smell, taste, hearing, and _____.
   - Ⓐ memory
   - Ⓑ thought
   - **Ⓒ touch**

2. A magnet will pick up a _____.
   - Ⓐ plastic fork
   - **Ⓑ steel nail**
   - Ⓒ wooden bowl

3. The Earth is made up of _____ layers.
   - Ⓐ two
   - Ⓑ three
   - **Ⓒ seven**

4. Sound is made when an object _____.
   - Ⓐ heats
   - Ⓑ cools
   - **Ⓒ vibrates**

5. Clouds are made of tiny drops of _____.
   - Ⓐ weather
   - **Ⓑ water**
   - Ⓒ dirt

6. Too much sugar can cause tooth _____.
   - Ⓐ paste
   - **Ⓑ decay**
   - Ⓒ candy

7. A _____ is a storm that has a funnel shape.
   - Ⓐ hurricane
   - Ⓑ volcano
   - **Ⓒ tornado**

8. Your _____ allows you to remember things.
   - **Ⓐ memory**
   - Ⓑ heart
   - Ⓒ computer

GO ON ⇨

Name _Matthew Balasa_ Date _____

Overall Assessment, page 2

Directions   Read the selection. Then, darken the circle by the answer that correctly completes each statement.

Benjamin Franklin believed that lightning was the same as electricity. Most people thought that this was a foolish idea. Franklin flew a kite during a storm so he could get electricity from the lightning. He proved his theory was right.

9. Why did Franklin fly his kite during a storm?
   Ⓐ He was a foolish man.
   Ⓑ He wanted to prove his theory.
   Ⓒ He thought that people were foolish.

10. Franklin thought that lightning was the same as _____.
    Ⓐ thunder
    Ⓑ rain
    Ⓒ electricity

11. Franklin proved that his theory was _____.
    Ⓐ foolish
    Ⓑ wrong
    Ⓒ correct

All things are made of matter. Matter takes up space. It comes in different forms. It may be a solid, like wood. It may be a liquid, like milk. It may be a gas, like air.

12. All things are made of _____.
    Ⓐ wood
    Ⓑ milk
    Ⓒ matter

13. Air is a _____.
    Ⓐ solid
    Ⓑ liquid
    Ⓒ gas

14. Matter takes up _____.
    Ⓐ space
    Ⓑ time
    Ⓒ stains

GO ON ⇨

Overall Assessment, page 3

Directions Read the selection. Then, write a complete sentence to answer each question.

You might think that mosquitoes read travel advertisements. They seem to appear at all the lakes and ponds as soon as the weather is warm. Mosquitoes do not visit these places for pleasure. They are born there.

Mosquitoes lay their eggs in fresh water. The water can be in a quiet corner of a pond, in a ditch, or in an old tire. A puddle will do, too. When the eggs hatch, the young don't look like mosquitoes at all. In this stage of their life cycle, the young are called *wrigglers*, and they look like tiny caterpillars. Wrigglers can't fly like adult mosquitoes. They breathe through a tiny tube like a snorkel that sticks out of the water. Wrigglers find many tiny organisms to feed on in water.

15. Why are so many mosquitoes found near ponds and lakes?

as soon as the weather is warm.

16. What does a mosquito look like when it first comes out of the egg?

the young don't look like mosquites at all

17. How do young mosquitoes breathe?

They breathe through a tiny tube like a snorkel that sticks out of the water.

STOP

Name _Matthew Balasa_   Date _____

Life Science Pretest   **Your Score:** _____

Directions Darken the circle by the answer that correctly completes each statement.

⏱ **You have 20 minutes.**

1. The sense of touch allows you to feel temperature, pressure, and _____.
   - Ⓐ pain
   - Ⓑ color
   - 🅒 smell

2. The _____ is the body part that identifies the messages of all the senses.
   - 🅐 heart
   - Ⓑ brain
   - Ⓒ liver

3. The _____ vibrates and sends messages about sounds to the brain.
   - Ⓐ cornea
   - Ⓑ outer ear
   - 🅒 eardrum

4. Ears of corn grow on a _____.
   - 🅐 stalk
   - Ⓑ shelf
   - Ⓒ head

Directions Read the selection. Then, darken the circle by the answer that correctly completes each statement.

Animals need energy to live and grow. Animals get their energy from the food they eat. Food is only one of the things that animals need in order to continue living. Most animals also need water to drink and oxygen to breathe. Land animals get oxygen from the air they breathe. Animals also need a place to live. Some animals, such as birds, build their own shelters.

5. An animal's body produces energy from _____.
   - Ⓐ air
   - 🅑 food
   - Ⓒ water

6. Animals that live on land get oxygen from _____.
   - Ⓐ the air
   - Ⓑ the water
   - 🅒 food they eat

7. Birds build their own _____.
   - Ⓐ cars
   - Ⓑ trees
   - 🅒 shelters

GO ON ⇨

Life Science Pretest, page 2

Directions   Read each selection. Then, write a complete sentence to answer each question.

Yeast is a single-celled plant. If you add sugar and warm water, the yeast plants grow and give off tiny gas bubbles. These gas bubbles cause the bread dough to expand and rise in the pan. Baking the bread stops the yeast plant from growing any more.

8. What causes bread dough to rise? _Yeast, sugar, warm water_

_____

9. What causes the yeast plant to stop growing? _Baking the_ _bread stops the yeast plant from growing any more_

People try to control mosquitoes by spraying chemicals to kill them. These chemicals may harm birds and other animals. A safer way to control mosquitoes is to drain ponds and puddles where they lay their eggs. However, this may be harmful to other wildlife that lives in ponds. Other ways to control the pests include encouraging natural enemies, like certain flies, bats, or fish, or spreading diseases that kill mosquitoes.

10. Why is the practice of draining ponds to kill mosquitoes not always a good idea?

Mosquitoes is to ponds and puddles where they lay their eggs

11. What methods for controlling mosquitoes might be better for the environment?

Other ways to control the pests include encouraging natural enemies like flies, bats, or spreading diseases that kill mosquitoes.

STOP

Name *Matthew Balasa*　　　Date *Feb, 28, 2008*

Earth Science Pretest　　Your Score: _____

Directions Darken the circle by the answer that correctly completes each statement.

⏱ **You have 20 minutes.**

1. The pull that keeps us on the Earth is _____.
   - Ⓐ gravity
   - Ⓑ tides
   - Ⓒ friction

2. The Moon moves in an orbit around _____.

   - Ⓐ the Earth
   - Ⓑ the Sun
   - Ⓒ Saturn

3. _____ is a part of the water cycle.
   - Ⓐ Weather
   - Ⓑ Precipitation
   - Ⓒ Tornado

4. A _____ is used to measure temperature.
   - Ⓐ forecaster
   - Ⓑ barometer
   - Ⓒ thermometer

Directions Read the selection. Then, darken the circle by the answer that correctly completes each statement.

The Earth is made of three layers. The center of the Earth is called the core. It is very hot. The middle layer is called mantle. The core heats the mantle. The outer layer is called the crust. It is solid and thinner than the other layers. The crust is made of rock and soil. We live on the crust of the Earth.

5. The Earth is made of _____ layers.
   - Ⓐ three
   - Ⓑ two
   - Ⓒ five

6. We live on the _____ of the Earth.
   - Ⓐ core
   - Ⓑ mantle
   - Ⓒ crust

7. The mantle is heated by the _____.
   - Ⓐ crust
   - Ⓑ volcano
   - Ⓒ core

GO ON ⇨

Name _____   Date _____

Earth Science Pretest, page 2

Directions   Read each selection. Then, write complete sentences to answer the questions.

Tornadoes usually form in the spring or summer. Cool, dry air moves down from the north. Warm, moist air moves up from the south. When the two kinds of air meet, the warm air begins to cool. As it cools, it can form a twisting cloud shaped like a funnel. The wind begins to swirl around the funnel. A tornado has begun. The winds move very fast, up to 300 miles per hour.

8. What causes tornadoes to form? _____

_____

_____

9. How fast do tornado winds blow? _____

_____

One form of air pollution is called smog. It is made up of smoke that is trapped near the Earth. Smog can irritate the eyes, nose, throat, and lungs. It can also make it hard for some people to breathe.

10. What is smog made of? _____

_____

11. How can smog hurt people? _____

_____

_____

_____ **STOP**

Physical Science Pretest Your Score: _____

Directions Darken the circle by the answer that correctly completes each statement.

⏱ **You have 20 minutes.**

1. A magnet will pick up an object that is made of _____.
   Ⓐ plastic
   Ⓑ iron
   Ⓒ wood

2. Which of the following can magnets pick up?
   Ⓐ paper clips
   Ⓑ rubber bands
   Ⓒ small pieces of paper

3. Butter in a hot frying pan _____.
   Ⓐ freezes
   Ⓑ melts
   Ⓒ screams

4. Work is done when _____.
   Ⓐ a force moves an object
   Ⓑ nothing moves
   Ⓒ a person holds something

Directions Read the selection. Then, darken the circle by the answer that correctly completes each statement.

A screw is a kind of inclined plane. It forms a spiral by winding around an inclined plane. Screws can hold things together, make holes, or help lift things. The screw forces the wood around the inclined plane to move apart, making a hole.

5. A screw is a kind of _____.
   Ⓐ lever
   Ⓑ inclined plane
   Ⓒ force

6. A screw forms a _____ around an inclined plane.
   Ⓐ wall
   Ⓑ fence
   Ⓒ spiral

7. The screw forces the wood to _____, making a hole.
   Ⓐ move apart
   Ⓑ stick together
   Ⓒ fall apart

GO ON ⇨

Physical Science Pretest, page 2

Directions Read each selection. Then, write a complete sentence to answer each question.

Oxygen is in the air. We need oxygen to breathe, and fire needs oxygen to burn. Also, oxygen causes iron and steel to rust.

8. Why do humans need oxygen? _____

_____

9. What does oxygen do to iron and steel? _____

_____

Air is a mixture of several gases. Oxygen is one of the gases in air. It takes fuel, oxygen, and heat to make a fire burn. The oxygen changes the fuel into a different kind of gas.

10. What is air? _____

_____

11. What does a fire need to burn? _____

_____

12. What does oxygen do to the fuel in a fire? _____

_____

Life Science Posttest   Your Score: _____

Directions Darken the circle by the answer that correctly completes each statement.

⏱ **You have 35 minutes.**

1. The tongue can taste bitter, sweet, salty, and _____ flavors.
   - Ⓐ pepper
   - Ⓑ pizza
   - ● sour

2. Too much sugar can cause tooth _____.
   - Ⓐ paste
   - ● decay
   - Ⓒ candy

3. A _____ diet gives you the right amount of food from the five basic food groups.
   - Ⓐ fat
   - Ⓑ working
   - Ⓒ balanced

4. Your heart beats faster when you _____.
   - Ⓐ run
   - Ⓑ sleep
   - Ⓒ read a book

5. It is very important to wear _____ when riding a bicycle.
   - Ⓐ a watch
   - Ⓑ dark clothing
   - Ⓒ a helmet

6. Features that living things have are called _____.
   - Ⓐ faces
   - Ⓑ traits
   - Ⓒ groups

7. Giving birth to live young and having fur are traits of _____.
   - Ⓐ reptiles
   - Ⓑ amphibians
   - Ⓒ mammals

8. An animal's _____ are suited to the kind of food it must eat.
   - Ⓐ legs
   - Ⓑ claws
   - Ⓒ teeth

GO ON ⇨

Name _____ Date _____

Life Science Posttest, page 2

Directions Read each selection. Then, darken the circle by the answer that correctly completes each statement.

Scientists know that beaks of birds are adapted for the different food each kind of bird eats. The heron uses its long beak like a pair of tweezers to snatch fish from the water. The sparrow uses its tough, blunt beak like a nutcracker to crack seeds. The woodpecker uses its strong, thick beak like a pickax to dig insects out of wood.

9. The _____ has a long beak to catch fish.
    Ⓐ owl
    Ⓑ heron
    Ⓒ crow

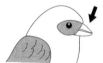

10. The sparrow has a tough, _____ beak.
    Ⓐ sharp
    Ⓑ long
    Ⓒ blunt

11. The woodpecker uses its beak to dig _____ from wood.
    Ⓐ insects
    Ⓑ nails
    Ⓒ leaves

Chocolate is made from the beans of the cacao tree. The cacao tree grows in the rain forests of Central and South America. It also grows in other warm places, such as Africa. The beans are found inside football-shaped pods. Each leathery pod holds about 50 beans. After the beans are picked, they are left to dry in the sun. Drying helps them to last longer.

12. Chocolate is made from the beans of the _____.
    Ⓐ chocolate bush
    Ⓑ cacao tree
    Ⓒ cocoa plant

13. The beans are found inside leathery _____.
    Ⓐ shoes
    Ⓑ footballs
    Ⓒ pods

14. After the beans are picked, they are _____ in the sunlight.
    Ⓐ dried
    Ⓑ burned
    Ⓒ eaten

GO ON ⇨

Life Science Posttest, page 3

Directions Read the selection. Then, write a complete sentence to answer each question.

Along the edge of many rivers and lakes, tiny craters dot the sandy bottom. These craters are sunfish nests. The nests are safe places for sunfish eggs to hatch.

The male sunfish is the nest builder. First, the male finds a safe place for the nest. Then, he swims in circles, fanning the water with his fins and tail. The powerful strokes move the sand. A small hole forms. The nest is finished.

After the nest is made, the female arrives. She lays eggs in the nest and leaves. The male guards the nest.

15. Why do sunfish need a nest? _____

_____

16. Which fish builds the nest, the male or the female? _____

_____

17. What does the sunfish do first before building the nest? _____

_____

18. How does the fish make the nest? _____

_____

19. What does the female sunfish do? _____

_____

GO ON ⇨

Name _____ Date _____

Life Science Posttest, page 4

Directions   Read the selection. Then, use the graph to answer each question. Write your answers in complete sentences.

A number of one-celled organisms living in the same place is called a population. These organisms are a lot like people. All populations change just as ours does. The graph shows the population growth of a simple organism over time.

20. How many organisms were there on the first day? _____

_____

21. What happened to the population after 20 days? _____

_____

22. How many organisms were in the population at 15 days? _____

_____

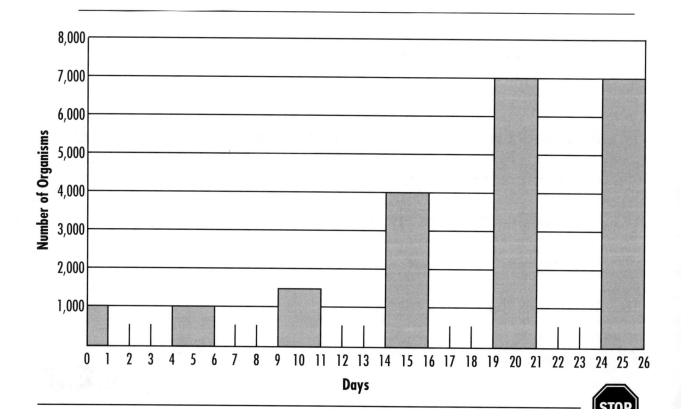

Name _____ Date _____

Earth Science Posttest Your Score: _____

Directions Darken the circle by the answer that correctly completes each statement.

You have 35 minutes.

1. A sudden movement in the Earth's crust is _____.
   Ⓐ an erosion
   Ⓑ a volcano
   Ⓒ an earthquake

2. The melted rock that flows from a volcano is called _____.
   Ⓐ lightning
   Ⓑ lava
   Ⓒ glue

3. Weather forecasters use many _____ to tell us about the weather.
   Ⓐ tricks
   Ⓑ games
   Ⓒ instruments

4. Forecasters can tell how hot or cold it will be. They can tell in which _____ the wind is blowing.
   Ⓐ house
   Ⓑ direction
   Ⓒ window

5. A _____ is a storm that brings heavy rains, high winds, and big waves.
   Ⓐ blizzard
   Ⓑ hurricane
   Ⓒ tornado

6. The liquid in a thermometer rises when the temperature _____.
   Ⓐ is cold
   Ⓑ is warm
   Ⓒ stays the same

7. The _____ is halfway between the North Pole and the South Pole.
   Ⓐ equator
   Ⓑ erosion
   Ⓒ evaporation

8. The breaking down and carrying away of soil is _____.
   Ⓐ moisture
   Ⓑ humidity
   Ⓒ erosion

GO ON ⇨

Earth Science Posttest, page 2

Directions Read each selection. Then, darken the circle by the answer that correctly completes each statement.

Cirrus clouds are high above the Earth. They are usually seen in fair weather. They are wispy and streak the sky. Cumulus clouds are white and fluffy. They look like cotton balls. They are often seen in good weather. But they can produce rain showers or snow. A thunderhead is a very tall cumulus cloud. Stratus clouds are low, dark clouds. They are seen close to the Earth. They often produce rain or snow.

9. _____ clouds are low and dark.
   Ⓐ Cirrus
   Ⓑ Cumulus
   Ⓒ Stratus

10. Cirrus clouds are usually seen in _____.
    Ⓐ fair weather
    Ⓑ bad weather
    Ⓒ the movies

11. A _____ is a very tall cumulus cloud.
    Ⓐ tornado
    Ⓑ snowflake
    Ⓒ thunderhead

Rocks change and break. The breaking of rocks into pieces is called weathering. One way weathering occurs is when rainwater and carbon dioxide gas mix in the air. The water falls to the ground and goes into cracks. The rainwater makes the rocks break.

12. The breaking of rocks into pieces is called _____.
    Ⓐ evaporation
    Ⓑ weathering
    Ⓒ thunder

13. One kind of weathering is when rainwater and _____ gas mix.
    Ⓐ oxygen
    Ⓑ natural
    Ⓒ carbon dioxide

14. The rainwater makes the rocks _____.
    Ⓐ pretty
    Ⓑ break
    Ⓒ old

GO ON ⇨

Earth Science Posttest, page 3

Directions   Read the selection. Then, write a complete sentence to answer each question.

Every day we take many things for granted. One thing we take for granted is water. No plant or animal could live without water. It is needed for drinking, cleaning, and keeping us cool. Our bodies are about two thirds water. We need about a quart of water a day to replace the water we lose naturally. All the food we eat and the things we use every day required much water in their making.

Americans use a half trillion gallons of water a day. Each person in the United States uses about 90 gallons of water a day for cleaning and gardening. Two more gallons per person are used for drinking and cooking. Factories use lots of water to make goods. It takes 60,000 gallons of water to make one ton of steel. Farmers use 115 gallons of water to grow the wheat for one loaf of bread, and 4,000 gallons are needed to get one pound of beef. As you can see, water is very important to us all. We must always be sure to take care of the water we have.

15. How much water does it take to grow the wheat for one loaf of bread?

_____

16. How much water does it take to produce one pound of beef?

_____

17. How much water do people need to drink in one day?

_____

18. How many gallons of water do Americans use in one day?

_____   **GO ON** ⇨

Earth Science Posttest, page 4

Directions This picture graph shows the number of known moons for each planet. Use the graph to answer the questions. Write a complete sentence to answer each question.

Number of Known Moons of the Planets

Mercury	
Venus	
Earth	○
Mars	○ ○
Jupiter	○ ○ ○ ○ ○ ○ ○ ○ ○ ○ ○ ○ ○ ○ ○ ○
Saturn	○ ○
Uranus	○ ○ ○ ○ ○
Neptune	○ ○
Pluto	

Code: ○ = 1 moon

19. How many moons does Uranus have? _____

_____

20. Which planets have no known moons? _____

_____

21. Which planet has the most moons? _____

_____

22. Which two planets have the same number of moons? _____

_____

_____ **STOP**

Physical Science Posttest Your Score: _____

Directions Darken the circle by the answer that correctly completes each statement.

⏱ **You have 35 minutes.**

1. Current moves easily through _____.
   Ⓐ a conductor
   Ⓑ a charge
   Ⓒ an open switch

2. The source of electricity in a flashlight is the _____.
   Ⓐ switch
   Ⓑ dry cell
   Ⓒ bulb

3. Objects with static electricity can pick up _____.
   Ⓐ paper
   Ⓑ heavy objects
   Ⓒ iron

4. An inclined plane that winds around in a spiral is a _____.
   Ⓐ lever
   Ⓑ wedge
   Ⓒ screw

5. Steel wool pads rust faster when they are _____.
   Ⓐ left outside in the rain
   Ⓑ in a cardboard box on the grocery shelf
   Ⓒ kept in an airtight can

6. Sugar would dissolve most easily in water that is at _____.
   Ⓐ 0° C (32° F)
   Ⓑ 18° C (64° F)
   Ⓒ 100° C (212° F)

7. A spring scale is used to measure _____.
   Ⓐ speed
   Ⓑ distance
   Ⓒ force

8. A drinking straw works because of differences in air _____.
   Ⓐ planes
   Ⓑ pressure
   Ⓒ conditioning

GO ON ⇨

Physical Science Posttest, page 2

Directions   Read each selection. Then, darken the circle by the answer that correctly completes each statement.

A force is a push or pull. Forces can be measured. Just as distances are measured in units called meters, forces are measured in units called newtons. When you push or pull on something, you apply a force to it.

9. A force is a _____.
- Ⓐ hop or skip
- Ⓑ weight
- Ⓒ push or pull

10. Distances are measured in units called _____.
- Ⓐ forces
- Ⓑ meters
- Ⓒ newtons

11. Forces are measured in units called _____.
- Ⓐ distance
- Ⓑ meters
- Ⓒ newtons

Electric currents can move through some materials more easily than others. Material that a current can move through is called a conductor. Most metals conduct electricity. They are like a wire that a current moves through. Your body is also a good conductor. Every circuit needs a generator, a conductor, and an electrical user.

12. A material that an electric current can move through is called a _____.
- Ⓐ conductor
- Ⓑ generator
- Ⓒ shock

13. Most _____ conduct electricity.
- Ⓐ woods
- Ⓑ metals
- Ⓒ rocks

14. Your _____ is a good conductor.
- Ⓐ book
- Ⓑ lunch
- Ⓒ body

GO ON ⇨

Physical Science Posttest, page 3

Directions   Read the selection. Then, write a complete sentence to answer each question.

Do you know what keeps us standing on Earth? Why don't we fall off? Why do things feel heavy? It is all because of gravity. Many years ago, a scientist discovered gravity. His name was Sir Isaac Newton.

Gravity is the pull that keeps things together. The larger a thing is, the more gravity it has. That is why we stay on Earth. It has a lot of pull. It pulls all objects toward it. That is why things feel heavy. Earth is pulling on everything we lift.

The Moon is not as large as Earth. That is why astronauts who go to the Moon feel lighter. When they jump, they stay in the air longer. The Moon does not pull them back as strongly as Earth does. The Moon does pull on Earth's oceans. The gravity of the Moon causes the oceans to move back and forth. This is what makes high tide and low tide.

Gravity affects all things, from little ants to the planets around us. Gravity is an amazing force!

15. Why is Earth's gravity so strong? _____

_____

16. Why can astronauts jump higher on the Moon? _____

_____

17. What is gravity? _____

_____

GO ON ⇨

Physical Science Posttest, page 4

Directions Read the selection. Then, use the chart to answer each question. Write a complete sentence to answer each question.

Petroleum has many uses. Gasoline, heating fuel, plastics, detergents, and drugs are just a few things that are made from petroleum.

Most countries do not produce as much petroleum as they use. So they must import, or bring in, the petroleum they need from other countries. Look at the chart below. It shows how much petroleum is produced in different places. It also shows how much petroleum is used in these places.

Place	Petroleum Produced	Petroleum Used
Middle East		
Europe and Russia		
USA and Canada		
Latin America		
Asia		
Africa		

18. Where is most of the petroleum produced? _____

_____

19. What areas use almost as much petroleum as they produce?

_____

20. What area must bring in most of the petroleum it uses?

_____

Name _____   Date _____

Life Science, part 1   **Your Score: _____**

Directions Darken the circle by the answer that correctly completes each statement.

**Testing Tips**

First, read the sentence carefully. Try each answer choice in the blank. Choose the answer that best completes the sentence.

Sample:

The oil from _____ can cause a skin rash.

Ⓐ poison ivy

Ⓑ oak trees

Ⓒ foxglove plants

Answer

The correct answer is *A. poison ivy*. The oil from this plant can cause a painful rash.

Now Try These

⏱ **You have 10 minutes.**

1. People must have _____ to see.
   Ⓐ glasses
   Ⓑ light
   Ⓒ ears

2. Your heart beats more slowly when you _____.
   Ⓐ run
   Ⓑ dance
   Ⓒ sleep

3. Animals are classified into two large groups by dividing those who have _____ from those who do not.
   Ⓐ wings
   Ⓑ fur
   Ⓒ backbones

4. _____ live part of their lives on water and part on land.
   Ⓐ Amphibians
   Ⓑ Mammals
   Ⓒ Birds

5. Behaviors that do not have to be learned are called _____.
   Ⓐ camouflage
   Ⓑ defense
   Ⓒ instincts

6. Flying south in the winter is called _____.
   Ⓐ hibernation
   Ⓑ migration
   Ⓒ protection

Life Science, part 2   Your Score: _____

Directions   Read each selection. Then, darken the circle by the answer that correctly completes each statement.

✦ Testing Tips

Look at the questions before you read the selection.
After you read the selection, read each question again.
Read all the answer choices.
Choose the answer that goes best with the selection.
Check your answers by looking back at the selection.

Now Try These

🕐 **You have 15 minutes.**

The Arctic is a very cold place. Ice and snow cover the land for most of the year. Yet snowy owls and polar bears make their homes there. These animals are fit to live in the Arctic. A bear has fur to help keep it warm. An owl has down feathers. Down feathers are soft and fluffy. They are close to the bird's body.

1. The Arctic has lots of _____.
   Ⓐ parks
   Ⓑ ice and snow
   Ⓒ sand storms

2. A bear has _____ to keep it warm.
   Ⓐ a stove
   Ⓑ a coat
   Ⓒ fur

3. An owl's down _____ are soft and fluffy.
   Ⓐ feathers
   Ⓑ fur
   Ⓒ hair

GO ON ⇨

Life Science, part 2, page 2

Directions Read the selection. Then, darken the circle by the answer that correctly completes each statement.

Animals exhibit a variety of behavior adaptations, both defensive and social, that help them survive. Animals behave in many different ways for many different reasons. Some animal behaviors help animals protect themselves from predators. Different animals have different ways of defending themselves. Some animals use camouflage to hide. Some, such as impalas, run away from predators. Some animals, such as giraffes, zebras, and musk oxen, stay together in large groups called herds. Staying in herds makes it harder for a predator to hunt just one animal. Some animals, such as porcupines and skunks, have body parts that help defend them. Opossums have a unique defense—they pretend to be dead.

4. The way an animal behaves is _____.
   - Ⓐ hibernation
   - Ⓑ an adaptation
   - Ⓒ protection

5. For many animals, running away is their best _____.
   - Ⓐ defense
   - Ⓑ behavior
   - Ⓒ camouflage

6. Some animals keep safe by _____.
   - Ⓐ living in groups
   - Ⓑ staying out in the open
   - Ⓒ swimming upstream

STOP

On a separate sheet of paper, write how you did and what you could do to improve.

Life Science, part 3   Your Score: _____

Directions   Read the selection. Then, write a complete sentence to answer each question.

⭐ Testing Tips

Look at the questions before you read the selection.
After you read the selection, read each question again.
Think carefully about the answer to each question.
Write your answer using complete sentences.
Check your answers by looking back at the selection.

Now Try These

🕐 **You have 30 minutes.**

While you are sleeping, you are unconscious. You do not know what is happening around you. Your body organs, such as your heart, lungs, and kidneys, keep working while you sleep. But most body functions slow down. Your breathing becomes slower. So does the beating of your heart. Your body temperature drops, too.

1. Why might you need a blanket or cover while you are sleeping?

   _____

   _____

2. Why don't you know what is happening around you as you sleep?

   _____

   _____

3. What happens to your body functions when you sleep? _____

   _____

GO ON ⇨

Life Science, part 3, page 2

Directions   Read the selection. Then, write a complete sentence to answer each question.

Exercise is important for everyone. If you do not use your muscles, you will become weak. Even astronauts must exercise. Since their bodies are not working against the full force of gravity, they hardly use their muscles in space. Bones and muscles get weak where there is not much gravity.

In 1970, three Soviet cosmonauts, who had been in space for 18 days, had to be carried from their spacecraft because their muscles were too weak to move their bones. Now astronauts exercise in space. They use a treadmill on which they can run in place against a moving track. Using the treadmill makes their arm and leg muscles work harder. By walking on the treadmill for 15 to 30 minutes each day, they keep their bones and muscles healthy.

Working out on the treadmill is a form of aerobic exercise. Aerobic exercise forces the body to use a large amount of oxygen over a long period of time. If you are in good health, you should do some form of aerobic exercise at least three times a week for at least 15 minutes without stopping.

4. Why do astronauts need to exercise in space?

_____

_____

5. How does the treadmill help astronauts?

_____

_____

GO ON ⇨

Life Science, part 3, page 3

Directions   Read the selection. Then, use the graph and write a complete sentence to answer each question.

Some trees grow faster than others. Some trees live longer than others. Those that live longest and grow fastest have the biggest trunks. The graph shows how big five different kinds of trees can grow. The measurement used to compare them is the diameter. *Diameter* is the distance through the center of the trunk.

Tree Diameters

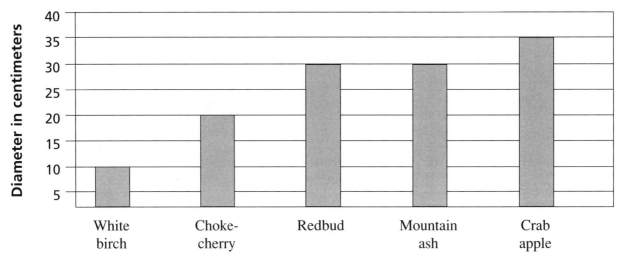

Types of Trees

6. Which fully grown tree has the smallest trunk? _____

_____

7. Which two trees can grow to have the same diameter? _____

_____

8. Which tree can grow the largest trunk? _____

_____

GO ON ⇨

Life Science, part 3, page 4

Directions Read the selection. Then, write a complete sentence to answer each question.

Have you ever seen a koala at a zoo? Maybe you saw a mother koala with her young peeking out of her pouch. The koala is a *marsupial*. A female marsupial is a mammal with a pouch on her belly. Marsupials develop inside the mother's body for only a short time. At birth, a koala is poorly developed and almost helpless. It has no fur, and its skin is pink. It cannot see. It is only about as long as the tip of your finger and weighs less than the eraser on a pencil. As soon as it is born, the tiny koala crawls several centimeters up through its mother's fur into her pouch.

Only one koala is born at a time. Once inside the pouch, the koala fastens its mouth onto a nipple to get the milk it needs. The young koala stays attached to the nipple inside the pouch for five to six months. Then, it climbs out of the pouch, but it still clings to the mother's chest. Next, the mother begins to feed her young some eucalyptus leaves. In a few weeks, the young koala stops drinking milk and eats only leaves.

Why do most people have to go to the zoo to see a koala? Koalas and many other kinds of marsupials live only in Australia and on the islands around it. Only one marsupial, the opossum, lives somewhere else. Opossums live in North and South America.

If you have seen a newborn kitten, you know it is very different from a newborn koala. Usually, four or five kittens are born at one time. They leave their mother's body at birth. They cannot see or hear. So they depend on their mother to nurse, clean, and protect them. Each kitten finds one of its mother's nipples to drink milk it needs. The kittens do not stay attached to the nipple, though. After 7 to 10 days, the kittens' eyes open. Their teeth begin to appear. At about three weeks, they start to walk and explore. About a week later, they begin to eat solid food.

GO ON ⇨

Life Science, part 3, page 5

Directions Read the selection. Then, write complete sentences to answer each question.

9. Why must a koala crawl into its mother's pouch and stay there after it is born? _____

_____

_____

10. When is a young koala able to leave its mother's pouch?

_____

_____

11. How does the food of the young koala change when it leaves the pouch? _____

_____

12. How is a koala at birth different from a kitten at birth?

_____

_____

_____

13. How are the first four weeks of life different for a kitten than for a young koala? _____

_____

_____

On a separate sheet of paper, write how you did and what you could do to improve.

Earth Science, part 1   Your Score: _____

Directions Darken the circle by the answer that correctly completes each statement.

Testing Tips

First, read the sentence carefully. Try each answer choice in the blank. Choose the answer that best completes the sentence.

Sample:

_____ is a part of the water cycle.
- Ⓐ Weather
- Ⓑ Precipitation
- Ⓒ Tornado

Answer

The correct answer is *B. Precipitation*. Precipitation is one of the three parts of the water cycle.

Now Try These

⏱ **You have 10 minutes.**

1. _____ are strong storms that only last a few minutes.
   - Ⓐ Energy
   - Ⓑ Hurricanes
   - Ⓒ Tornadoes

2. Earth's _____ is caused by temperature, clouds, and rain.
   - Ⓐ air pressure
   - Ⓑ weather
   - Ⓒ air

3. A _____ is a long period of not enough rain.
   - Ⓐ hurricane
   - Ⓑ drought
   - Ⓒ tornado

4. The top layer of the Earth is called the _____.
   - Ⓐ core
   - Ⓑ crust
   - Ⓒ mantle

5. _____ is the breaking down and carrying away of rocks and soil.
   - Ⓐ Evaporation
   - Ⓑ Watering
   - Ⓒ Erosion

6. In a solar eclipse, the Moon moves between _____ and the Sun.
   - Ⓐ Venus
   - Ⓑ the Earth
   - Ⓒ the North Star

STOP

Earth Science, part 2   Your Score: _____

Directions   Read the selection. Then, darken the circle by the answer that correctly completes each statement.

⚡ Testing Tips

Look at the questions before you read the selection.
After you read the selection, read each question again.
Read all the answer choices.
Choose the answer that goes best with the selection.
Check your answers by looking back at the selection.

Now Try These

⏱ **You have 15 minutes.**

The nine planets are all very different from each other. One reason is their distance from the Sun. Mercury is closest to the Sun. It is very hot there during the day. At night, it gets very cold. Pluto is the farthest from the Sun. It is sometimes covered with a layer of ice. At other times, it orbits closer to the Sun. Then some of the ice melts. Venus is the second planet. Earth and Mars are next. Jupiter is the largest planet. It is the fifth planet from the Sun. Saturn, the sixth planet, is known for its rings. Uranus and Neptune are the seventh and eighth planets.

1. What planet is closest to the Sun?
    Ⓐ Mercury
    Ⓑ Mars
    Ⓒ Pluto

2. Which planet has rings?
    Ⓐ Pluto
    Ⓑ Saturn
    Ⓒ Neptune

GO ON ⇨

Earth Science, part 2, page 2

Directions   Read the selection. Then, darken the circle by the answer that correctly completes each statement.

Just imagine! If big rocks had not been broken into little bits, we would not have any food to eat. That is because all the soil on our Earth— the dirt in which we plant flowers and vegetables and grain—is formed largely from rocks that have been crushed by wind, rain, and storms. Of course, many other things are mixed with the ground-up rocks to make rich soil. It took hundreds of thousands of years to make our soil.

Some soil is full of pebbles that are larger than grains of sand. This soil is called gravel. Other soil is sandy. Some other soil, called clay, is made up of bits even smaller than sand. These bits are so small that you can hardly see them.

3. How is soil formed?
   Ⓐ from clay
   Ⓑ from pebbles
   Ⓒ from rocks that have been crushed

4. What do we call pebbles that are larger than grains of sand?
   Ⓐ gravel
   Ⓑ rocks
   Ⓒ clay

5. What is clay made of?
   Ⓐ broken rocks
   Ⓑ things mixed with ground-up rock
   Ⓒ bits even smaller than sand

6. Why do people want to take care of soil?
   Ⓐ They don't like it when the wind blows.
   Ⓑ It takes hundreds of thousands of years to make soil.
   Ⓒ There is too much gravel.

On a separate sheet of paper, write how you did and what you could do to improve.

Name _____   Date _____

Earth Science, part 3   Your Score: _____

Directions   Read the selection. Then, write a complete sentence to answer each question.

⭐ **Testing Tips**

Look at the questions before you read the selection. After you read the selection, read each question again. Think carefully about the answer to each question. Write your answer using complete sentences. Check your answers by looking back at the selection.

Now Try These

🕐 **You have 30 minutes.**

Every day we take many things for granted. One thing we take for granted is water. No plant or animal could live without water. It is needed for drinking, cleaning, and keeping us cool. Our bodies are about two thirds water. We need about a quart of water a day to replace the water we lose naturally. All the food we eat and the things we use every day required much water in their making.

Americans use a half trillion gallons of water a day. Each person in the United States uses about 90 gallons of water a day for cleaning and gardening. Two more gallons per person are used for drinking and cooking.

1. What three things do humans use water for?

_____

_____

2. How much of our bodies is water?

_____

3. How much water do people need to drink in one day?

_____

Earth Science, part 3, page 2

Directions   Read the selection. Then, write a complete sentence to answer each question.

An eclipse of the Sun is called a solar eclipse. During a solar eclipse, the Moon moves directly between the Earth and the Sun. The Moon shuts out the view of the Sun. The shadow of the Moon falls on Earth.

A solar eclipse starts when the Moon begins to pass in front of the Sun. At first, it blocks only a small part of the Sun from view. Soon, almost the entire surface of the Sun is hidden. (This is called a total eclipse.) The daytime sky darkens. For a few minutes it seems as if it is late evening. Then, more and more of the Sun becomes visible as the Moon continues to move. The eclipse ends when the Moon no longer blocks the Sun.

Scientists can learn a lot about the Sun during a solar eclipse. However, a total eclipse cannot be seen from any one spot for longer than 7 minutes and 40 seconds. That doesn't give the scientists much time to make their observations. So during a solar eclipse in 1973, a group of scientists took their equipment aboard a jet. The jet sped across the sky, all the time staying in the Moon's narrow shadow. These scientists were able to study a total eclipse for 74 minutes.

4. What is a solar eclipse? _____

_____

5. What causes a solar eclipse? _____

_____

_____

6. How long can a total eclipse be seen from one place? _____

_____

GO ON ⇨

Earth Science, part 3, page 3

Directions Read the selection. Then, write a complete sentence to answer each question.

There are nine planets in our solar system. The word *planet* came from the Greek word for *wanderer*. The ancient Greeks thought the planets wandered in space. They did not know that each planet moved in its own orbit around the Sun.

All the planets, except Earth, were named for gods or a goddess in Roman and Greek myths. Listed are the planets and the gods they were named for.

Planet	Roman or Greek god
Mercury	Messenger of the gods
Venus	Goddess of love
Mars	God of war
Jupiter	Ruler of the gods
Saturn	God of agriculture
Uranus	First ruler of the heavens
Neptune	God of the sea
Pluto	God of the dead

7. What does the word *planet* mean in Greek? _____

_____

8. How do planets move? _____

_____

9. Which planet was named for the god of agriculture? _____

_____

10. Which planet was named for a goddess? _____

_____

GO ON ⇨

Earth Science, part 3, page 4

Directions   Read the selection. Then, use the graph and write a complete sentence to answer each question.

You can't see air. It is made up of invisible gases. Two of these gases—nitrogen and oxygen—make up almost all of the air. Most living things cannot survive without oxygen. For example, we need oxygen to help our bodies get energy from the food we eat.

Living things need nitrogen to make new cells, but they cannot take the nitrogen directly from the air. Nitrogen must first be combined with other elements. The air contains other gases, too, such as carbon dioxide. We give off carbon dioxide when we breathe out and when we burn fuel. Carbon dioxide and the other gases besides nitrogen and oxygen make up just one part in a hundred parts of air.

Look at the pie graph. Do you know what *percent* means? *Percent* (%) means "parts per hundred." There are 100 cents in a dollar. One way to think about *percent* is to think that one dollar is made up of 100 pennies. You know that 78 cents is a large part of a dollar.

Air is free; you don't have to pay for it. But suppose you did have to pay for air. For every dollar you spent on air, 78 cents would go for nitrogen.

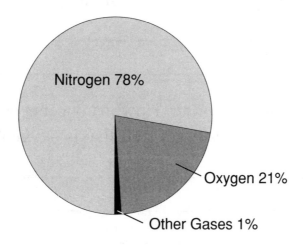

GO ON ⇨

Earth Science, part 3, page 5

Directions   Read the selection. Then, use the graph on page 37 and write a complete sentence to answer each question.

11. How much of the air is made up of nitrogen? _____

_____

_____

12. Which gas makes up 21 percent of the air? _____

_____

13. How much of the air is made up of other gases? _____

_____

14. We breathe in oxygen and give off carbon dioxide. Is there more oxygen or more carbon dioxide in the air? _____

_____

_____

15. Which gas makes up the largest part of air? _____

_____

_____

16. Suppose you had to pay for air. How many cents out of every dollar you spent would you pay for the part that is oxygen?

_____

_____   **STOP**

On a separate sheet of paper, write how you did and what you could do to improve.

Name _____   Date _____

Physical Science, part 1 Your Score: _____

Directions Darken the circle by the answer that correctly completes each statement.

 **Testing Tips**

First, read the sentence carefully. Try each answer choice in the blank. Choose the answer that best completes the sentence.

Sample:

Matter keeps its own shape when it is in the form of _____.
- Ⓐ a solid
- Ⓑ a liquid
- Ⓒ a gas

Answer

The correct answer is *A. a solid*. Only in the solid form does matter hold its shape.

Now Try These

You have 10 minutes.

1. What machine is being used in the picture?
   - Ⓐ inclined plane
   - Ⓑ lever
   - Ⓒ screw

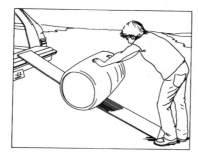

2. This machine makes work easier because it _____.
   - Ⓐ has a sharp point
   - Ⓑ has a slanted surface
   - Ⓒ moves slowly

3. Another name for this machine is a _____.
   - Ⓐ spring scale
   - Ⓑ ramp
   - Ⓒ lever

4. All of theses are the same form of matter except _____.
   - Ⓐ milk
   - Ⓑ oil
   - Ⓒ steam

5. If a circuit is open, _____.
   - Ⓐ a light will go on
   - Ⓑ all the parts are connected
   - Ⓒ the switch may be off

Physical Science, part 2 Your Score: _____

Directions Read the selection. Then, darken the circle by the answer that correctly completes each statement.

Testing Tips

Look at the questions before you read the selection.
After you read the selection, read each question again.
Read all the answer choices.
Choose the answer that goes best with the selection.
Check your answers by looking back at the selection.

Now Try These

You have 15 minutes.

A force that acts between objects even when they are not touching is gravity. All objects pull on other objects. Earth's gravity pulls on everything on Earth's surface and in the atmosphere. It also pulls on everything else in the solar system and the universe. The force of Earth's pull on an object can be measured. This measurement is the object's weight. You have weight because Earth's gravity is pulling on you.

1. Magnetism is a force that can act between objects that aren't touching. Another force that works the same way is _____.
   Ⓐ wind
   Ⓑ gravity
   Ⓒ friction

2. Gravity is a _____.
   Ⓐ lifting force
   Ⓑ pushing force
   Ⓒ pulling force

GO ON ⇨

Physical Science, part 2, page 2

Directions   Read the selection. Then, darken the circle by the answer that correctly completes each statement.

Anything that takes up space and has mass is matter. Air is matter. The amount of matter that is present in an object is called mass. Everything on or near Earth that has mass is pulled toward Earth's surface. The force that pulls objects toward Earth's surface is gravity. You can measure how much gravity is pulling on an object. This measure is called weight.

Even though you don't think about air having mass, it does. So, air also has weight. The weight of air pressing down on an area is air pressure. There is a column of air about 160 kilometers high pressing down on you right now. Because air is all around you, it pushes against your body in all directions. Instruments have been developed that can measure air pressure. These instruments are called barometers.

3. A ball filled with air weighs
_____ one that is empty.
Ⓐ more than
Ⓑ less than
Ⓒ the same as

4. Air presses against you
_____.
Ⓐ now and then
Ⓑ never
Ⓒ all of the time

5. The measure of gravity's pull on an object is called _____.
Ⓐ mass
Ⓑ weight
Ⓒ matter

6. An instrument to measure air pressure is called a _____.
Ⓐ scale
Ⓑ kilometer
Ⓒ barometer

On a separate sheet of paper, write how you did and what you could do to improve.

Physical Science, part 3 Your Score: _____

Directions   Read the selection. Then, write a complete sentence to answer each question.

Testing Tips

Look at the questions before you read the selection.
After you read the selection, read each question again.
Think carefully about the answer to each question.
Write your answer using complete sentences.
Check your answers by looking back at the selection.

Now Try These

You have 30 minutes.

A physical change is a change when the molecules of a substance do not change. The substance can be torn, cut, melted, evaporated, or condensed. A chemical change is a change when the properties of a substance change. The molecules become something else. For example, burning a log causes a chemical change. The log changes to ashes, smoke, and other kinds of gases.

1. What is a physical change? _____

_____

2. What is a chemical change? _____

_____

3. What kind of change is a log burning? _____

_____

GO ON ⇒

Physical Science, part 3, page 2

Directions   Read the selection. Then, write a complete sentence to answer each question.

If you listen to a weather report on television or radio, you'll find out how warm or cold it probably will be, and you'll learn if rain or snow is expected. But you can also find out how clean or dirty the air is. This condition of the air is called air quality.

Air quality depends on how much pollution is in the air. Air pollution is caused when harmful solid particles or gases get into the air. Vehicles such as cars, trucks, and buses burn fuel and give off exhaust. In the vehicle exhaust, there are gases and particles of liquids or solids. Some energy plants burn fuels such as coal or oil to make electricity. The burning fuels release gases and solids into the air, which also add to air pollution. Some factories use a lot of chemicals or metals to make things. Gases and tiny bits of metal are sent into the air through the factories' smokestacks. Not all air pollution is caused by people. Some is caused by natural events, such as forest fires and the eruption of volcanoes.

4. What is air quality? _____

   _____

5. How does air become polluted? _____

   _____

   _____

6. How can natural events cause air pollution? _____

   _____

GO ON ⇨

Name _____ Date _____

Physical Science, part 3, page 3

Directions   Read the selection. Then, write a complete sentence to answer each question.

Suppose a ball was flying through the air and there was no such thing as friction. What if no forces pulled or pushed the ball? It would just go on moving forever and ever. The ball, or any other object, would maintain its motion until some outside force acted on it. This is a property that all objects—and all matter—share.

This property is called inertia. You can observe inertia in action when you ride in a car. When the car starts moving, you feel the back of the seat push against you so that you start moving, too. When the car slows down, the friction between you and the seat slows you down as well. If the car stops suddenly, you feel the seat belt pull against you and slow you down.

7. What is inertia? _____

_____

_____

8. What is required to stop an object in motion? _____

_____

9. Suppose you were in a parked bus and there was a tennis ball on the floor of the bus. What would happen to the ball if the bus started moving forward? Explain your answer.

_____

_____

GO ON ⇨

Physical Science, part 3, page 4

Directions   Read the selection. Then, write a complete sentence to answer each question.

Everything around you is matter—the chair you are sitting on, the air around you. You are matter, too. All matter has some things in common. For instance, all matter takes up space. Matter is commonly found on Earth in one of three states—solid, liquid, and gas. Matter in each of these states has different properties.

A *solid* has a definite shape. It also has a definite volume. That is because its particles are very close together and are in a regular pattern. The particles move within the solid, but they are held together by an attraction. Heating a solid causes its particles to move more rapidly, weakening the attraction between them, and melting occurs.

A *liquid* does not have a definite shape. However, it does have a definite volume. The particles that make up a liquid move more rapidly and freely than those in a solid. The attraction between them is not as strong as the attraction between the particles in a solid, and the particles tumble over and around each other. A liquid flows and takes the shape of the container into which it is poured.

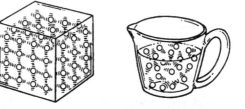

A *gas* does not have a definite shape or volume. The particles that make up a gas move rapidly and freely. They don't have much attraction for one another. A gas spreads out to fill its container. The air around you is a gas.

GO ON ⇨

Physical Science, part 3, page 5

Directions   Read the selection. Then, write a complete sentence to answer each question.

10. What are the three states of matter? _____

_____

11. Which state of matter has a definite shape and a definite volume?

_____

_____

12. Which state of matter does not have a definite shape or volume?

_____

_____

13. How is a liquid different from a gas? _____

_____

_____

14. How is a solid different from a liquid? _____

_____

_____

_____

On a separate sheet of paper, write how you did and what you could do to improve.

Answer Key

Overall Assessment, pages 2–4
1. C, **2.** B, **3.** B, **4.** C, **5.** B, **6.** B, **7.** C, **8.** A, **9.** B, **10.** C, **11.** C, **12.** C, **13.** C, **14.** A, **15.** They hatch from eggs laid in the water., **16.** It looks like a tiny caterpillar., **17.** They breathe through a tiny tube that sticks out of the water like a snorkel.

Life Science Pretest, pages 5–6
1. A, **2.** B, **3.** C, **4.** A, **5.** B, **6.** A, **7.** C, **8.** The yeast plants give off tiny gas bubbles that cause the bread dough to rise in the pan., **9.** Baking the bread stops the yeast plant from growing any more., **10.** Other kinds of wildlife could be harmed., **11.** One better method would be to spread natural enemies or diseases that kill mosquitoes.

Earth Science Pretest, pages 7–8
1. A, **2.** A, **3.** B, **4.** C, **5.** A, **6.** C, **7.** C, **8.** Tornadoes form when warm, moist air meets cool, dry air. The warm air cools and forms a twisting cloud shaped like a funnel. The wind begins to swirl around the funnel., **9.** Tornado winds can blow up to 300 miles per hour., **10.** Smog is made of smoke trapped near the Earth., **11.** Smog can irritate the eyes, nose, throat, and lungs. It can also make it hard for some people to breathe.

Physical Science Pretest, pages 9–10
1. B, **2.** A, **3.** B, **4.** A, **5.** B, **6.** C, **7.** A, **8.** Humans need oxygen to breathe., **9.** Oxygen makes iron and steel rust., **10.** Air is a mixture of several gases., **11.** A fire needs fuel, oxygen, and heat to burn., **12.** The oxygen changes the fuel into a different kind of gas.

Life Science Posttest, pages 11–14
1. C, **2.** B, **3.** C, **4.** A, **5.** C, **6.** B, **7.** C, **8.** C, **9.** B, **10.** C, **11.** A, **12.** B, **13.** C, **14.** A, **15.** The nest is a safe place for sunfish eggs to hatch., **16.** The male fish builds the nest., **17.** He finds a safe place to build the nest., **18.** He fans the water with his fins and tail until a hole forms in the sand., **19.** She lays the eggs in the nest, then leaves., **20.** There were 1,000 organisms on the first day., **21.** The population stopped growing., **22.** There were 4,000 organisms on the fifteenth day.

Earth Science Posttest, pages 15–18
1. C, **2.** B, **3.** C, **4.** B, **5.** B, **6.** B, **7.** A, **8.** C, **9.** C, **10.** A, **11.** C, **12.** B, **13.** C, **14.** B, **15.** Farmers use about 115 gallons of water to grow the wheat for one loaf of bread., **16.** About 4,000 gallons of water are needed to get one pound of beef., **17.** People need to drink one quart of water a day., **18.** Americans use about a half trillion gallons of water a day., **19.** Uranus has five moons., **20.** Mercury, Venus, and Pluto have no known moons., **21.** Saturn has the most moons., **22.** Mars and Neptune have the same number of moons.

Physical Science Posttest, pages 19–22
1. A, **2.** B, **3.** A, **4.** C, **5.** A, **6.** C, **7.** C, **8.** B, **9.** C, **10.** B, **11.** C, **12.** A, **13.** B, **14.** C, **15.** Earth's gravity is strong because Earth is so large., **16.** They can jump higher because the Moon has less gravity., **17.** Gravity is the pull that keeps things together., **18.** Most of the petroleum is produced in the Middle East., **19.** Latin America and Africa produce about as much as they use., **20.** The U.S.A. and Canada must bring in most of the petroleum they use.

Life Science, part 1, page 23
1. B, **2.** C, **3.** C, **4.** A, **5.** C, **6.** B

Life Science, part 2, pages 24–25
1. B, **2.** C, **3.** A, **4.** B, **5.** A, **6.** A

Answer Key, page 2

Life Science, part 3, pages 26–30

1. You might need a blanket or cover because your body temperature drops as you sleep., **2.** You don't know what is happening around you because you are unconscious while you are sleeping., **3.** Your body functions slow down while you are sleeping., **4.** Astronauts need to exercise because when they are in space, their bodies do not work against the full force of gravity, and their bones and muscles get weak., **5.** The treadmill makes their arm and leg muscles work harder., **6.** The white birch tree has the smallest trunk., **7.** The redbud tree and the mountain ash tree grow to about the same diameter., **8.** The crab apple tree can grow the largest trunk., **9.** The baby koala is poorly developed and almost helpless. It gets milk and protection from its mother., **10.** A young koala can leave the pouch after five or six months., **11.** After leaving the pouch, the young koala eats eucalyptus leaves., **12.** A koala at birth is very tiny, has no fur, and is almost helpless, while a kitten is much larger, has fur, and is better developed., **13.** The kitten drinks milk from its mother off and on. Its teeth begin to appear. It walks around and explores for itself. It starts to eat solid food. The young koala stays attached to a nipple inside its mother's pouch.

Earth Science, part 1, page 31

1. C, **2.** B, **3.** B, **4.** B, **5.** C, **6.** B

Earth Science, part 2, pages 32–33

1. A, **2.** B, **3.** C, **4.** A, **5.** C, **6.** B

Earth Science, part 3, pages 34–38

1. Humans use water for cleaning, drinking, and keeping cool., **2.** Our bodies are about two thirds water., **3.** People need to drink one quart of water a day., **4.** A solar eclipse is a time when most of the Sun is hidden by the Moon., **5.** A solar eclipse is caused when the Moon moves between the Earth and the Sun., **6.** A total eclipse can be seen in one place for up to 7 minutes and 40 seconds., **7.** The word *planet* means wanderer in Greek., **8.** The planets move in orbits around the Sun., **9.** Saturn was named for the god of agriculture., **10.** Venus was named for the goddess of love., **11.** The air is 78% nitrogen., **12.** Oxygen makes up 21% of the air., **13.** About 1% of the air is made up of other gases., **14.** There is much more oxygen in the air than there is carbon dioxide., **15.** Nitrogen makes up the largest part of air., **16.** The part that is oxygen would cost 21 cents.

Physical Science, part 1, page 39

1. A, **2.** B, **3.** B, **4.** C, **5.** C

Physical Science, part 2, pages 40–41

1. B, **2.** C, **3.** A, **4.** C, **5.** B, **6.** C

Physical Science, part 3, pages 42–46

1. A physical change is a change when the molecules of a substance do not change., **2.** A chemical change is a change when the properties of a substance change., **3.** Burning a log causes a chemical change., **4.** Air quality is how clean or dirty the air is., **5.** Air pollution is caused when harmful solid particles or gases get into the air., **6.** Forest fires and the eruption of volcanoes can put harmful particles and gases into the air., **7.** Inertia is the property of an object continuing to move until some outside force acts on it., **8.** Some outside force, such as friction, is required to stop an object in motion., **9.** It would roll toward the back of the bus, because there would not be anything to push against it to make it move with the bus., **10.** The three states of matter are solid, liquid, and gas., **11.** A solid has a definite shape and a definite volume., **12.** A gas does not have a definite shape or volume., **13.** A liquid has a definite volume, but a gas does not., **14.** A solid has a definite shape, but a liquid does not.

www.svschoolsupply.com
© Steck-Vaughn Company

48

Answer Key
Higher Scores on Science Standardized Tests 3, SV 3420-7